Multiple Mini Interview Questions Book

MSC MEDICAL

ISBN (978-0-9878272-0-3)

How to use this book

This workbook has been designed specifically to help the reader learn, practice, and apply various interview strategies to maximize success in real multiple mini interview (MMI) scenarios.

The examples given here should be taken as illustrations and are not intended to depict the perfect answer. In fact, there is no right or wrong answer in the MMI.

In the first section, **A Crash Course in Ethics,** a general overview of the main ethical principles involved in the MMI is provided. This is only meant to provide a simplified explanation of the underlying ethical principles and should be supplemented by other resources including books that exclusively focus on the subject.

The **Introduction** section describes the MMI process and outlines general strategies for answering the scenarios.

Chapters 1 – 3 introduce the various types of MMI scenarios, each accompanied by thorough explanations on specific goals, responses, and tips for success. The explanations are accompanied by a sub-section titled, '**What to do inside the room**', which provides readers with carefully designed step-by-step instructions for responding to different types of MMI scenarios.

However, due to the unstructured nature of MMI scenarios not every step will be relevant to every scenario, and the steps may need to be adapted to fit a particular scenario.

Chapter 4 includes specialized MMI scenarios designed by MSC MEDICAL to mimic the interview stations commonly used by most universities. Although the cases focus on diverse fields such as medicine, nursing, pharmacy, dentistry and physiotherapy, the main topics apply to interviews for admission to all health-related programs. **Therefore, it is highly recommended that every scenario be attempted regardless of the program you are being interviewed for.**

As mentioned earlier, there is no such a thing as a perfect answer in the MMI. **Consequently the aim of this book is only to provide sample responses, written by medical professionals, unrehearsed and under MMI conditions.** What this means is that each response should be studied carefully, and then adapted to the scenario at hand using the basic tips and strategies provided, changing the sample response to a perfect model response. Not only will this help sharpen interview skills, but it will also help personalize each response and boost the chances for overall success.

Sincerely,

MSC MEDICAL

Table of Contents

A Crash Course in Ethics

In order to become competent and comfortable in responding to MMI scenarios you must fully understand the four principles of medical ethics stated below:

1) Autonomy

Respect for individuals and their right to make decisions regarding their health and how they want to be treated. Ultimately, as long as the patient is deemed competent and his or her wishes regarding their treatment do not put anyone at risk, their wishes must be respected (even if they are refusing lifesaving treatment).

2) Beneficence

As health care professionals we must always act in the patient's best interest. As you will soon find out, in real life scenarios as well as MMI scenarios it's often difficult to precisely 'define' the patient's best interest. This is owed to the fact that every single patient has unique needs, wants, cultural background, etc.

3) Non-Maleficence

Perhaps you have heard of the phrase "first, do no harm". Non-maleficence basically means do not harm your patients. This ethical principle reminds us that the positive outcome of a treatment must always outweigh its negatives.

4) Justice

The principle of justice is related to fairness and equality regarding the distribution of health care resources (such as drugs, treatments, access to healthcare professionals, etc) in society. According to the principle of justice everyone in society deserves his or her fair share of medical resources.

In the MMI, almost all cases contain some form of a dilemma, which is often caused by a conflict between two or more of the four ethical principles discussed above. Thus, whenever you read an MMI scenario your primary objective should be to recognize the ethical principles involved and aim to explain a plan of action or a resolution strategy, which could be used to resolve the dilemma. In order to decide whether or not an alcoholic should be deprioritized for liver transplantation, for instance, one must take the following ethical principles into account:

Beneficence – transplanting the liver is the most suitable option to save the patient's life.

Justice – liver is a limited medical resource and many might argue that such a resource should be allocated where it will do the most good (i.e. be allocated to patients that will make the best use of it).

Non-Maleficence – not transplanting could very likely result in the patient's death.

Autonomy – given that patient is competent, he or she has the right to choose whether or not they want to have the transplant operation.

Introduction

Ever since the introduction of the Multiple Mini Interview (MMI) format by McMaster University, a significant number of programs have adapted to use MMI as a tool for assessing competitive applicants. As of 2011, MMI is used in Australia, Canada, United States, and United Kingdom by programs including medicine, nursing, pharmacy, and dentistry.

Being closely modeled after the objective standardized clinical examination (OSCE), the MMI is designed to enable evaluators (admission departments) to assess applicants' competencies in multiple contexts. Although the exact procedure under which MMI is conducted differs for each university, the general outline is shown below:

Instructions given to applicants before the interview:

- Applicants must leave all personal belongings in the locker room. No recording devices, cellular phones, or writing material is permitted in the interview.

- All applicants must sign the confidentiality agreement form (acknowledging that they agree not to discuss or disclose any information regarding the MMI process or scenarios with anyone).

1- The interview will consist of 10 stations (this number varies for different schools) situated in 10 different rooms.

2- Each station has unique instructions that must be followed closely. The instructions are posted on the door outside each station (they are also available inside each station, in case applicants need to refer back to them) and are generally covered by a piece of paper.

3- Once the interview begins, the applicants will be signalled (usually by a bell) to remove the paper covering the instructions and begin reading. They will be given 2 minutes (time varies for different schools) to read the instructions.

4- At the end of the two minutes the applicants are signalled (usually by a bell) to enter the room. They will be given 8 minutes (time varies for different schools) to carry out the instructions in the room.

5- At the end of the 8 minutes applicants are signalled (usually by a bell) to exit the room.

Applicants move to the next station and the above procedure (1-5) is followed.

The popularity of the MMI among different institutions and programs has resulted in its rapid evolution. Most schools have added their own 'spin' to the MMI, and consequently myriads of new and unique types of stations where applicants are asked to comment on a particular scenario, interact with another interviewee to complete a task, interact with the evaluator to complete a task, interact with an actor (role play), and respond to audio/video presentations, have emerged.

While different types of stations generally overlap with one another, there are three main types of MMI stations: (1) **standard**, (2) **acting**, and (3) **communication skills**.

Before we describe each of the three MMI stations in detail, it's essential that we discuss the importance of critical thinking skills in the MMI. Critical thinking skills are the most important set of skills needed for success in the MMI. While it's possible to attain an above-average score on most MMI stations without having much background knowledge in medical ethics or past/current issues in health care, the lack of effective critical thinking abilities greatly hinders one's performance.

Owed to the competitive nature of most health programs such as medicine, and the perceived importance of grade-point-average (GPA) by admission committees, many pre-health students rely on their memorization ability to succeed in exams and other forms of assessments. In the real world as well as in the MMI, however, in order to solve complex problems and succeed one must not only be able to recall vital information but also be able to apply such information in an effective way utilizing his or her critical thinking skills. **Critical thinking is the cognitive ability to: (1) evaluate an issue from a variety of perspectives and viewpoints, (2) remain open-minded to alternative interpretations, (3) be flexible to accept novel explanations if they explain the evidence better, are simpler, or have fewer inconsistencies, and (4) avoid making snap judgment.**

In most real-life tasks critical thinking abilities and memory go hand in hand, but given that the MMI has been designed to test anything but one's memory (applicants are always provided with a copy of the case during the interview), **critical thinking alone**

11

forms the cornerstone for success in all MMI stations. Thus, it is imperative that from this point on you train yourself to apply the cognitive abilities discussed above (1-4) to every MMI scenario you encounter.

In order to perform well in the MMI it is imperative that you are familiarized with different types of MMI stations. In the next sections (Chapter 1-4) a brief background as well as a response template is provided for different types of MMI stations.

Chapter One

Standard Stations

Background:

An issue (real or hypothetical) will be posted on the station door which you are to discuss with the interviewer. Interviewers have been provided with some background information on each station as well as 2-5 prompt questions. Depending on how you discuss the scenario and your timing, the interviewer may or may not ask you prompt questions. (It's perfectly normal if the interviewer does not ask you any prompt questions or vice versa).

Standard scenarios fall under two main categories: (1) ethical decision making and (2) critical thinking. Many of the standard scenarios share elements from both categories. Ethical decision making stations are ones that present you with specific ethical dilemmas which could be related to healthcare (a patient refusing treatment) or everyday life (your classmate cheating on an exam). Although critical thinking is indirectly assessed in all MMI stations, it's directly tested in critical thinking scenarios. Such scenarios are one of the least prevalent and most difficult types in the MMI. Critical thinking scenarios are ones which include abundant information and distracters (irrelevant terms, facts, or data).

What to do inside the room

Step 1: Summary

The first thing you should do after greeting the interviewer is to provide a brief summary of the case **in your own words** to demonstrate your understanding of the case. Many applicants read the case word by word for the interviewer. Although such approach is not wrong it certainly does not add much to your response. Summarizing the case using your own terminology and wording, however, enables the interviewer to assess how well you have understood the case. Additionally, if you have misunderstood anything about the scenario, the interviewer would, in most circumstances, assist you in understanding the scenario better.

Step 2: Key issue(s)

Mention the key issues involved in the case - provide a clear explanation of ethical as well as non-ethical questions and/or issues that are raised by the scenario. Additionally, identify the major dilemma(s). For example, in a scenario where a Jehovah's Witness is refusing a blood transfusion on behalf of his five-year-old daughter, one of the major dilemmas is the conflict between respecting patient's autonomy (in this case the father's decision regarding his daughter's treatment) and the healthcare professional's duty to save her life.

Step 3: Seek More Information

Ethical dilemmas are always open to a myriad of interpretations. This especially holds true in the MMI because usually scenarios contain a limited amount of information and are quite vague. For this reason MMI scenarios are challenging and no matter how you respond to them you are never right or wrong.

You should examine the scenario closely and make an effort to define the context in which the scenario is taking place. In order to do this effectively, you should ask yourself the following questions:
- Does the information provided in the case make it difficult for you to understand the situation and make a decision? If so why?
- Does the case fail to mention vital information or distort any aspect?
- Are there any ambiguities that affect your decision or resolution plan?
- What other ways can you interpret the scenario?
- Does the situation include relevant social, cultural, religious, or personal conflicts?

In this step you are striving to demonstrate to the interviewer that you are not the kind of applicant who makes snap judgments (the worst thing one can do in the MMI) and that you recognize the importance of remaining open-minded as well as evaluating different perspectives.

Therefore, your task is to discuss the scenario from as many perspectives as possible and clearly identify missing information, which is crucial in resolving the dilemma.

Step 4: Action*

In this step your aim is to clearly state your answer, opinion or decision regarding the case. In order to achieve this you should begin by suggesting 2-3 possible courses of action and describe the pros and cons for each one. (This gives you an opportunity to 'think out loud' and enables the interviewer to observe and assess your reasoning).

In addition to weighing the pros against cons that pertain to your suggested courses of action, you should make an effort to situate yourself in the scenario (put yourself in the shoes of those who will be affected by your decisions). Doing so enables you to personalize your answer and avoid personal biases that could influence your decision.

*Surprisingly many applicants fail to clearly state their answer(s) to scenarios due to a number of reasons such as simply forgetting, not being able to decide, not understanding the case or being afraid to come across as an opinionated person. Not answering the scenario affects your MMI score significantly. Therefore, it's absolutely crucial that you ultimately settle on a particular stance and clearly convey your proposed decision to the interviewer, even if you are unsure if it's the best answer.

Step 5: Take initiative

This is where your creativity and critical thinking abilities come into play. During the last minute or two of your time, given that you have discussed everything thoroughly and responded to all prompt questions, you should briefly summarize your response and follow through by taking initiative. In order to take initiative you must utilize your critical thinking abilities and creativity to come up with practical steps or suggestions which would assist you, or other people involved, in solving and preventing the underlying dilemma(s) from occurring in the future. (For example, in a case where a pregnant teenager caused irreversible damage to her unborn child as a result of drinking alcohol, you could wrap up your response by briefly suggesting that similar cases could be prevented in the future if we implement better education programs for young mothers). For most scenarios, possible areas in which you could propose changes include **policies, procedures, planning**, and **regulations**.

Chapter Two

Acting Stations

Background:

A scenario is posted on the door and you are asked to enter the room and interact with one or more actor(s) as if he or she is the person who has been mentioned in the scenario. In addition to the actor(s), there will be at least one evaluator in every acting station. The evaluator is never involved in the scenario or the discussion of the case. His or her duty is to only observe and rate your performance. Generally, you should avoid direct interaction with the evaluator unless instructed otherwise. Being used to shaking hands with the interviewers in standard stations, many applicants automatically try to greet the evaluator which usually results in an awkward situation. Thus, in acting stations, try your best to be in character as soon as you enter the room.

Things to remember

First impressions are a vital part of communicating with the actor(s). Many applicants are so nervous and feel pressed for time that they seem rushed when they greet the actor(s). In order to stand out from the rest of the applicants, your greeting should convey warmth and caring, especially if the scenario you are dealing with involves an actor who is in a vulnerable state (physically or emotionally). Thus, you should enter the room in a relaxed state of mind.

Facial expressions can help you convey and demonstrate your compassion, and concern for the actor to the evaluator. While your acting skills are not assessed, facial expressions enable you to demonstrate your personality and character, often better than verbal communication.

Head nods could be utilized to convey your understanding and attentiveness. However, many nervous applicants overdo them and come across as being impatient.

Touch can be used as a facilitative (establishing a friendly relationship with the actor) and/or a therapeutic (consoling the actor) tool in the acting scenarios. For example, let's say you are interacting with an actor who is role playing a nervous patient. You can simply place your hand on his or her shoulder to console them and demonstrate your empathy, non-verbally.

Many applicants try very hard to say and do as much as they can during acting scenarios. Such approach is disadvantageous because in acting scenarios a significant portion of the information and issues are meant to be delivered by the actors and by saying too much, an applicant will limit the amount of time the actor has to bring up vital information regarding the case. Thus, it's essential that you utilize **silence** and **active listening** as tools to give the actor adequate time to respond to your questions without jumping in with another question too quickly.

Questioning is one of the most important skills in acting scenarios. There are two main categories of questions that one could utilize in acting scenarios:

1) Open questions are used to encourage the actor to tell you about the case. Listening to them, and encouraging them to tell you as much as they can, is definitely a valuable investment of your time. However, in many scenarios actors will not give you much information in the beginning. Therefore, it's important that you do not get discouraged early on. Some examples of open questions include:

- How can I help you today?
- What has been troubling you lately?
- What brings you here today? What else can you tell me about your feelings?
- How could we work together to solve this problem?
- Why do you feel frustrated?

2) Closed questions should be used whenever you are trying to gain specific information. They often limit the actor to one or two-word responses. The best time to use such questions is whenever you feel you want to clarify something or clear misunderstandings. Some examples of closed questions include:

- Do you feel safe right now?
- Is this the first time this has happened to you?
- Would you like me to call one of your family members and ask them to come?
- What time did that happen?

What to do inside the room

Step 1: Question the actor

In a typical acting scenario you should start with open questions about the main issues involved, then narrow down your focus using closed questions to gather specific information. **It's very important that you do not start your interaction with the actor using closed questions – doing so will limit your approach as well as your options to discover important details about the case.**

Step 2: Summarize

Once you have gathered enough information you **summarize** by drawing together the significant aspects of what has been said. For instance, 'let me just go over what we discussed to make sure that I've got everything right'. Providing a summary to the actor is extremely important because it enables you to: clarify any misinterpretations, give the actor an opportunity to bring up anything he or she might have forgotten, and most importantly demonstrate to the evaluator that you have been actively listening.

Step 3: Make a decision or support your stance

Next, depending on the context of the scenario you have to either make a decision (for example, if you are role-playing a general manager who has to make a decision about firing an employee, you must make sure that you clearly state what your final decision is, before your time runs out) or clearly state your stance about the scenario. Especially in complex scenarios, many applicants get so caught up with playing their role and discussing the scenario with the actor that they forget to clearly state their stance or decision. This dramatically reduces their overall scores, regardless of how well they have interacted with the actor.

Breaking bad news

Background:

Sometimes in communication skills scenarios you are asked to deliver some form of bad news to an actor. Alternatively, you can be asked to describe how you would deliver bad news to someone, in a standard MMI station (which involves no role-playing or actors). Regardless of the setting, delivering bad news is a difficult task in the MMI.

In the past, students have been asked to: (1) give a terminal or life-changing prognosis such as telling someone that they have end-stage cancer, or telling a young mother that her son has passed away in a car accident, (2) deliver relatively less dramatic news but nonetheless one that is devastating to the patient such as telling an aspiring hockey player that he can no longer play hockey because he will never recover from his injury or fire a fellow employee because they came to work late.

On average, most applicants perform poorly on scenarios that involve breaking bad news mainly because they do not understand what they are being tested on. **The key to** performing well in such scenarios is to understand that breaking bad news is one of the most difficult aspects of working in healthcare and that the impact of the news will not only have **medical** but also **emotional, occupational, physical** and **cultural** implications. Thus, it's essential that whenever you are asked to deliver bad news in the MMI you consider all implications and make an effort to discuss them with the actor and if possible come up with a resolution.

From a healthcare professional's perspective, delivering bad news involves:

Preparation

It is essential to ensure that the patient is physically and mentally fit to hear and comprehend the news, prior to delivering bad news. In the event that he or she is deemed unfit, the priority should be to treat the underlying condition (for example, if the person that the bad news is being delivered to is under stress or is emotionally ill, he or she must first be treated and helped before the news is disclosed to them).

Checking own readiness

How a healthcare professional presents him or herself to the person who is receiving bad news, greatly affects the outcome. Looking stressed and tense could potentially heighten the news recipient's stress level. Therefore, it's important that the healthcare professional familiarizes him or herself with the recipient's past medical history, gather as much information as possible regarding the news, be prepared to address any question or concern that the news recipient might have, and develop a plan of how the news is to be delivered.

Appropriate setting

Although often overlooked, the setting in which bad news is delivered is equally as important as to how it's delivered. The most appropriate setting is a quiet, private room in which the recipient feels relaxed, and comfortable. In order to make the setting more suitable the healthcare professional could be accompanied by a fellow staff member, such as a social worker, and the news recipient be accompanied by a relative or a friend.

What to do inside the room

Step 1: Find out what the news recipient already knows

Prior to breaking the news, you should find out what the actor already knows and understands about the scenario and the news. This will enable you to understand the degree of insight and provide you with a baseline on which to build on. In some MMI scenarios, the actor is instructed to indicate that he or she suspects that something is seriously wrong. In such circumstances, you should use the opportunity to ask him or her some opening questions.

Step 2: Find out what the news recipient wants to know

In order to set yourself apart from other applicants, before you deliver the news you should always ask the actor what and how much he or she wants to know. This could be done by asking the actor directly. In real life scenarios for instance, some people prefer to not be told bad news about their health while others would want a thorough explanation with as much detail as possible. Consequently, by simply asking the actor what he or she prefers and explaining to them that its perfectly normal if they don't want to know everything, you will demonstrate to the evaluator that you are respecting the actor's autonomy.

Step 3: Deliver news

The news should be delivered clearly while avoiding bluntness. Begin by 'softly' warning the actor that you have some unpleasant news for him or her. For example, if you have been asked to tell someone that they have tested positive for HIV, you can say 'unfortunately your test results are more serious than we were expecting'.

i) Pause and allow the news recipient to process the information

At this point you should pause and enable the actor to process the information you delivered to them. In order to make sure that the evaluator understands why you are pausing, you should clearly explain to the actor that you want to give him or her as much time as they need to process and take in what they have been told. Additionally, you should seek the actor's permission to continue, for example you could say 'please take your time and let me know when and if you want me to continue'.

ii) Encourage news recipient to express his/her feelings or concerns

After delivering the news you should encourage the actor to share his or her concerns and feelings with you. This will enable you to demonstrate, to the evaluator, that you are empathizing with the actor.

iii) Take initiative

In the last minute or two of your time inside the room you should express your desire to work with the actor to plan a future course of action as well as why you believe it's important to do so. Depending on the scenario the next course of action could be to schedule a follow-up appointment or to offer additional support such as help from a social worker, counseling, etc.

Chapter Three

Communication skills stations

Background:

Over the past two decades the term "communication skills" has been gaining an immense level of popularity in the academic as well as the professional sector. In fact, "communication skills" is among the most repeated phrases in the qualification requirement section of every advertised job.

Due to the importance of effective communication skills in health care, there are usually 1-3 stations dedicated to assessing applicants' communication skills in the MMI. While such stations could vary in the format through which they are delivered they share one main objective: to gauge applicants' verbal and non-verbal communication skills.

Most of us are able to deliver effective instructions to family and friends, but not to strangers. Mainly because we are unaware of strangers' communication style, background, education level, and life experience. **The most common reason for performing poorly on MMI communication skills stations is not knowing and overestimating how much the other person you are communicating with, already knows.** In order to succeed in these stations you must appreciate and understand that effective communication involves much more than exchanging information. You must assume that the person you are communicating with has absolutely no background information about the information you are trying to convey to them and must make sure that you cover the most basic steps.

In communication skills stations you could be asked to give or receive instructions, or provide a description of some sort to a particular audience (for example, describe the importance of sleeping to a 5-year-old child).

What to do inside the room

Step 1: Describe the task

The first thing you should do is clearly describe the task for the other person you are interacting with, in your own words. This will clear-up any misunderstandings, and enables you to demonstrate your leadership skills to the evaluator.

Step 2: Agree on a plan of Action

Next, you should collaborate with the other person to come up with a strategy about how you plan on completing the task. This strategy should be as detailed as possible and work for both of you. Things you can discuss include how you are going to communicate, how much time you are going to spend on each part of the task, how you are going to give feedback to each other, etc. **In order to demonstrate your understanding of the importance of teamwork, to the evaluator, you should always express your desire to make decisions as a team rather than individually.**

Step 3: Anticipate difficulties

Briefly mention to your collaborator some difficulties that you expect to face in accomplishing the objectives. For example, if you have been asked to reproduce a detailed drawing you can simply inform your partner that given the amount of time available you are not certain whether or not you would be able to provide instructions for every detailed feature of the drawing.

Step 4: Give instructions

In order to provide effective instructions you must establish a logical instructional sequence. To achieve this you must break the task down into step-by-step procedures (don't just perform this in your head, make sure that both the evaluator and your collaborator understand what you are doing and why you are doing it). Only provide a small number of instructions at any one time – it's difficult for the average person to remember a large amount of information, especially during stressful situations like the MMI. Utilize direct and specific terminology and language. In other words say exactly what you mean and don't leave your collaborator guessing. Keep your instructions as simple as possible (an effective way to achieve this is to think of your collaborator as a 5-year-old child). If you are unsure whether or not your collaborator has understood you, politely ask him or her to repeat your instructions in his or her own words. Lastly, don't rush your instructions. **In giving/receiving instructions stations you are not assessed on how well you reproduce an image or what percentage of the task you complete but rather on the quality of your instructions and ability to communicate effectively**. Therefore, resist the urge to speak fast and jump from one instruction to another in an effort to save time.

Chapter Four

Practice Scenarios

We recommend that readers attempt to work through each
scenario under MMI conditions (2 minutes to read the scenario
and 6-8 minutes to respond), record their answers in the space
provided and finally review the appropriate comments and score
their performance utilizing the provided score sheets.

As mentioned earlier, there is no such a thing as a perfect answer
in the MMI. **Consequently the aim of this book is only to
provide sample responses, written by medical professionals,
unrehearsed and under MMI conditions**.

Being interviewed is a scary but exciting process. Be prepared
and put your best foot forward. And remember to have fun along
the way!

Score Sheet for Standard Stations

Assessor's Name _____

Date _____

Conflict of interest: Yes No

> Place
> Candidate's Label
> Here

Scoring Sheet for Station --

Applicant's ability to recognize the key issues:

Excellent   (Clearly states and addresses all of the main issues)

Good   (Clearly states and addresses most of the main issues)

Adequate   (Mentions and partially addresses some of the main issues)

Poor   (Does not mention or discuss the main issues)

Extremely Poor   (Does not recognize or address any of the issues)

Applicant's communication skills:

Excellent   (Conveys his/her response in an organized and coherent manner with appropriate amount of content)

Good   (Applicant's response is delivered with some degree of structure and suitable amount of content)

Adequate   (Applicant' response contains some relevant content but lacks structure)

Poor   (Applicant's response lacks structure and content)

Extremely Poor   (Applicant's response is repetitive and lacks structure and content)

Applicant's critical thinking ability:

Excellent   (Discusses the case from multiple perspectives while utilizing well-developed arguments)
Good   (Provides an effective answer backed by appropriate arguments)
Adequate   (Discusses the case only from one perspective but provides a complete answer)
Poor   (Provides an answer prior to developing an argument)
Extremely Poor   (Fails to provide any valid argument or an answer)

Applicant's suitability for a career in their chosen field:

Excellent
Adequate
Poor
Extremely Poor

Please score each category by following the scheme below:
Excellent 5
Adequate 4
Poor 2
Extremely Poor 1

Combined score for all categories: -- / 20

Case 1. Mr. Wang, a 55 year-old patient, has had back problems for over 3 years. He states that ever since his back pains started he has not been able to sit still for more than ten minutes. He has been on pain medications with minimal effect. His primary doctor, Dr. Ronaldson, believes that the only option left to entertain is back surgery. For various reasons, Mr. Wang is reluctant to undergo surgery, and instead asks the doctor to refer him to an acupuncturist. He tells Dr. Ronaldson that his insurance coverage requires a physician's approval for "alternative" therapy. Additionally, he mentions that his wife has been successfully treated by an acupuncturist before. Should Dr. Ronaldson write the referral?

Summary

_____

_____

Key issue(s)

_____

_____

Seek more information

_____

_____

_____

Action

_____

_____

_____

_____

Take initiative

_____

_____

_____

_____

Summary

A middle aged patient with chronic back pain, who has not had much luck with conventional therapy, is refusing his doctor's advice for back surgery and instead requests a referral to see an acupuncturist.

Key issue(s)

I believe the central issue here is that there is a conflict between Dr. Ronaldson's medical recommendation and Mr. Wang's request for alternative treatment. A patient might want all kinds of treatments and therapies, some of which might be effective and some of which might actually be harmful. Must the physician automatically comply?

Additionally, the case touches on the issue of patient autonomy.

Seek more information

Before delving into proposing a resolution and deciding whether or not he should write the referral, I think it's important that Dr. Ronaldson keeps an open-mind and first explores the case further by seeking more information regarding Mr. Wang's concerns, values and preferences. Some possible reasons behind Mr. Wang's request for alternative medicine and refusal of surgery include: (1) lack of pleasant or desirable experience with conventional medicine (maybe Mr. Wang is dissatisfied with the side effects of the painkillers), if that's the case then he could be prescribed different painkillers, (2) it's possible that he is simply interested in acupuncture solely based on his wife's recommendation, (3) Mr. Wang might have lived or grew-up in a country or a region, such as China where people are accustomed to alternative forms of medicine and (4) Mr. Wang may simply be afraid of surgery, in which case appropriate measures could be made to ensure that he is comfortable before, during and after surgery. Ideally, by taking time to actively listen to Mr. Wang, Dr. Ronaldson would be able to make a better decision regarding the referral as well as strengthen the patient-doctor relationship.

Action

Next, Dr. Ronaldson should thoroughly educate Mr. Wang about his condition and the factors which necessitate back surgery, while utilizing simple and easy-to-understand language. He should explain his professional opinion and recommendation to Mr. Wang by highlighting the difference between western medicine and alternative medicine and his un-biased opinion regarding the two, while remaining sensitive to Mr. Wang's cultural values and beliefs.

Additionally, Dr. Ronaldson could utilize other resources to educate both himself and Mr. Wang regarding the use of acupuncture. Such resources could be reliable articles or studies about acupuncture.

Now, for the sake of argument, if we assume that Mr. Wang continues to ask for the referral, despite Dr. Ronaldson's efforts to address his concerns regarding back surgery, Dr. Ronaldson's next step would depend on how comfortable he is about writing the referral. Because, ultimately as a physician he has to do what he believes is best for his patient. Thus, if Dr. Ronaldson knows enough about the risks and benefits of acupuncture therapy for

Mr. Wang's back issues and believes that Mr. Wang would benefit from it, then he is justified to write the referral. Conversely, if for any reason, he doesn't consider acupuncture therapy to be the best course of treatment for Mr. Wang he should not feel pressured or obligated to write the referral. However, even if Dr. Ronaldson decides against writing the referral, he is still responsible for Mr. Wang's well-being. Thus, instead of offering a blanket refusal about writing the referral and dismissing Mr. Wang, he should do whatever he can to further assist him. For example, he could refer him to a colleague who knows more about acupuncture therapy and is open to write a referral. In other words, even though it's paramount that Mr. Wang's autonomy is respected, here it should not take precedent over Dr. Ronaldson's professional belief and values. Conversely, the opposite would hold true if instead of asking for a referral Mr. Wang was competently requesting that his current treatment be terminated.

Patients like Mr. Wang are often in a vulnerable state and desperate to try almost anything. Therefore, it's very important that Mr. Wang is made aware of the possibility of becoming a victim of medical frauds that could potentially cost him money, time and health.

Take initiative

Finally, this case in spite of being challenging, provides a valuable learning opportunity for Dr. Ronaldson. In order to ensure that he is prepared to deal with similar issues in the future and better able to assist his patients, he could: (a) learn more about alternative medicine and create a list of accredited health care professionals who specialize in alternative medicine (such resources could be invaluable for patients like Mr. Wang), and (b) develop an internet forum or a discussion board where patients could help each other (non-medical related advice) and utilize each other's experiences regarding alternative medicine.

Case 2. Mrs. A is a patient in your dental clinic. In spite of going above and beyond to help her and accommodate to all her needs, she always complains and when it comes to paying her fees she often makes unreasonable excuses. One day you receive a release form from Mrs. A which states that she wants her medical records to be sent to another dentist. Additionally she states that she will try her best to pay the outstanding balance that she owes your clinic, by next year. Would you respect her wish and release her records to another dentist?

Key issue(s)

_____

_____

Seek more information

_____

_____

_____

Action

_____

_____

_____

_____

_____

Take initiative

_____

_____

_____

_____

Prompt questions

Do you feel that the other dentist should be made aware of this patient's past behavior?

If you were the other dentist would you want to know about a new patient's past financial record?

Case 3. In this station you will interact with another person to complete a task. Your role is to give verbal instructions to the person in the room so he or she can reproduce the image seen below. The person in the room has not seen this image and will rely only on your verbal instructions to reproduce the image. Once you enter the room you will sit with your back against his or her back and will be provided with a copy of this image. You must take extra care that the other person does not see the image and refrain from turning around during this exercise. Your performance will be evaluated by the evaluator who will be sitting to your left.

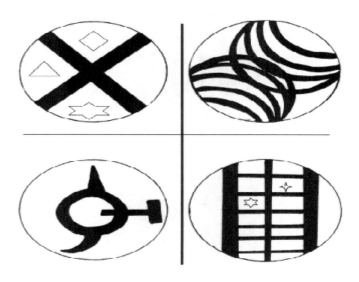

Step 1: Describe the task

_____

Step 2: Agree on a plan of Action

_____

_____

_____

Step 3: Anticipate difficulties

_____

Step 4: Give instructions

_____

_____

_____

Step 5: Take initiative

_____

_____

Describe the task

The task is for **us to collaborate as a team** to reproduce this image that I have in front me. Does that sound clear to you? Do you have any questions?

Agree on a plan of Action

Now, before we start, I believe it's a good idea to quickly come up with a plan of action that **we both** agree on. First, let's make sure that we both stop each other and ask questions whenever we feel something is unclear or not working well. In order to be as efficient as possible, I will start by describing the overall features of the image and then if time allows describe the details. I will only give you instructions for a small section of the image at a time and to avoid mistakes I want you to wait after I completely deliver each set of instructions before you start drawing.

To avoid confusion I will say "done" after each set of instructions. So whenever you hear me say "done" you can proceed to draw. Similarly, I will only move on to the next set of instructions after you finish drawing the previous sections and say "next". Do you know what I mean? So I will give you the instructions for a small section and then say "done" and then you draw that section and say "next" and so on.

This way we keep things simplified and minimize the need for corrections.

So far so good?

Anticipate difficulties

Now, I should warn you that given the amount of time that we have been given and the complexity of the image, I might not be able to give you instructions for every little detailed feature. But I will try my best to do as much as possible. Is that okay?

Give instructions

I should give you a general sense of what I am looking at here before you start drawing things. I have a standard size (A4) piece of white paper which is divided into four equal sized quadrants (do you know what I mean by quadrants?). In each of the four quadrants there is an abstract shape. Additionally, the whole image is printed in black and white.
Okay?

Now let's start. First can you tell me what sort of drawing equipments you have been provided with? For example do you have a ruler, compass, etc?

All right!

Can you turn your paper so it's in landscape (where you have the horizontal sides longer than the vertical sides)? Now, please divide the page into four equal sized quadrants by drawing two lines, one running horizontal and the other vertical. The vertical line is approximately three times as thick as the horizontal line. Overall it looks as if the horizontal line was drawn with a regular pencil while the vertical one was done by one of those permanent markers, which are somehow thicker. Okay "done" now you can draw.

Now, since we are facing opposite directions my left is actually your right and vice-versa. To avoid confusion I will always refer to things from your point of view. So, if I say left, I mean your left not mine.

Next, I want you to draw four identical circles in the centre of each of the four quadrants. Each circle should approximately cover 3/4 of the area of the quadrant they are in. "Done"

Now in each circle there are different abstract objects. Let's start with the circle in the upper right quadrant. Draw an X in the centre of this circle. The arms of the X should be as long as the diameter of the circle, in other words the X should divide the circle into four equal quadrants. "Done"

There are four abstract shapes printed in each circle, which are all separated from each other by vertical and horizontal lines.....

-- End of time –

Case 4. A 98-year-old female patient comes to your dental clinic for a routine check-up. Her teeth seems healthy for her age and in your professional opinion don't need much work. To your surprise she requests a follow-up appointment for several expensive procedures including implants, and veneers. You inform her that these elective procedures would cost her approximately twenty thousand dollars. She insists that you go ahead and book the appointment for her and that she won't have a problem paying for the procedures. Should you respect her wish and fulfill her request?

Summary

_____

_____

Key issue(s)

_____

_____

Seek more information

_____

_____

Action

_____

_____

_____

_____

_____

Take initiative

_____

_____

_____

_____

Prompt questions

- Would your response change if the patient was a 21-year-old actress?

Key issue(s)

- Patient directed care.
- Essential medical procedures versus elective procedures.

Seek more information

Why is she requesting cosmetic procedures?
Is she competent to make decisions about her health and/or spending money?
Does she genuinely want the procedures or are there other underlying factors? Is she requesting these procedures as a form of rebellion against her family?
Does she have difficulty coming to terms with aging?

Action:

- Do not offer the procedures on the grounds that she is too old and doesn't need them. (Cons: undermining patient's autonomy and discrimination based on age. Pros: none).

- Offer the procedures without asking any questions. (Cons: might end up taking advantage of a vulnerable patient, patient might regret having the procedures done. Pros: short term satisfaction for patient, financial benefit for the doctor)

- Make a follow-up appointment to: understand the reason behind her request and whether or not she is competent, educate her about the procedures (risks and benefits) and ensure that she is making an informed decision. (Cons: none. Pros: strengthen doctor-patient relationship, enable patient to make an informed decision).

Ultimately given that the patient is deemed competent, she has every right to request the procedures. However, the doctor should only perform the procedures if he feels comfortable to do so and should not feel obligated to please the patient.

Take initiative

- Establish a clear line of communication between health care professionals and patients to avoid misunderstandings.

- Implement a protocol that calls for equal treatments of all patients regardless of their age, race, or socioeconomic status.

Case 5. Mr. J is 44 years old and works at a nuclear power plant. He lives at home with his two teenage daughters who occasionally have friends over. One evening Mr. J is admitted to the local hospital after falling on the stairs and suffering a fractured knee. Upon seeing the doctor he refuses to sign the release form for a knee surgery and says "just give me some painkillers doc. I cannot afford to miss work even for one day". Should his wish be granted? Why?

Summary

_____

_____

Key issue(s)

_____

_____

Seek more information

_____

_____

_____

Action

_____

_____

_____

_____

_____

Take initiative

_____

_____

_____

_____

Prompt questions

Should his refusal for surgery be reported to his supervisor at work? Why?

Key issue(s)

- Capacity and competency.
- Informed consent.
- Patient compliance.
- Respecting patients' autonomy and privacy.

Seek more information

Are there other reasons why Mr. J is not in favor of knee surgery? Is he afraid of the surgery or becoming a burden on his family?

Are there any alternative treatments?

What is Mr. J's position at the power plant? Does he depend on the use of his knee at work (he might have an administrator job which does not require much walking around)?

Why does he want to continue working? Are other factors at play or is it purely for financial reasons?

Is there anything preventing him from making an informed decision regarding his care?

Is he competent enough in making decisions about his health? Does he understand the full implications of refusing treatment?

Does Mr. J have access to an appropriate support system once he is discharged?

Action

- Discharge Mr. J and prescribe him pain killers. (Cons: negative health implications, possible risk at work. Pros: temporarily please patient by giving in to his demands)

- Take time to have a comprehensive discussion with Mr. J to: assess his competency, explain for him the full implications of his decision (including the possibility of irreversible damage to his knee and placing himself and/or his co-workers at risk), investigate why he is refusing treatment, and collaborate with him to find an appropriate form of treatment. (Cons: none. Pros: enable patient to make an informed decision, patient is included in planning his care).

- Ultimately, if surgery is the only viable option and in spite of all efforts Mr. J does not provide informed consent, his request must be respected. However, given the nature of his profession, the health care team must ensure that Mr. J's decision does not place his co-workers or anyone else at risk. If it does, Mr. J must be encouraged to disclose his injury to his supervisor at work. If he chooses not to report his injury himself, the health care team is justified to make a medical report on his behalf (safety of general public overrides Mr. J's right to privacy).

Take initiative

- Implement strategies to ensure that patients understand the implications of refusing treatment and how their decisions might affect others (in this case, possibly, Mr. J's colleagues as well as the general public).

Case 6 (Acting Stations). You are a new volunteer in a senior retirement house. Your first assignment is to visit with Mr. Asennase who is 87 years old. He is from a very small town in northern Canada. He tells you that he never cared much about technology but now that he has finally retired, he is curious to learn. The first thing he wants to learn about is internet. Please enter the room and greet Mr. Asennase and try your best to describe internet to him. **Keep in mind that he has never even heard of the word internet and has absolutely no background knowledge**

Step 1: Describe the task

_____

Step 2: Agree on a plan of Action

_____

_____

_____

Step 3: Anticipate difficulties

_____

Step 4: Describe internet

_____

_____

_____

_____

_____

_____

_____

Step 5: Take initiative

_____

_____

Case 7. You and another fellow student are shadowing a senior physician as part of a mandatory clinical rotation. During your second week you notice that the physician often speaks mandarin to his patients. Unable to understand mandarin you become frustrated and discuss the matter with the other student. Responding to how he feels about the situation, the other student replies, "I don't really care man, I just want to finish this rotation and get out of here". What would you do?

Summary

_____

_____

Key issue(s)

_____

_____

Seek more information

_____

_____

_____

Action

_____

_____

_____

_____

_____

Take initiative

_____

_____

_____

_____

Summary

A physician communicates with his patients in a language other than English, making it difficult for students and learners with understanding the conversation.

Key issue(s)

I believe this case is centered around two main issues: First, it involves student education and second, more importantly, patient care. While the case gives the impression that the second student is indifferent to his learning, the lack of understanding is having a direct effect on education of the first student.

Seek more information

Before making a decision and taking action, it is important to obtain a few more details regarding the patients and the physician. Are the patients equally fluent in both English and Mandarin? If so, do they have a preference for which language is used during the interaction? What about the physician? Can he or she speak fluently in both? Is the matter discussed in Mandarin medical in nature, or are the physician and patient making small-talk? Additionally, does the physician explain to the student what he or she is saying in Mandarin (either during or after the consult) or is the student left behind during the conversation? These questions are important because they help define what action needs to take place.

Furthermore, it is also prudent to find out whether the physician is aware of the responsibilities he or she has towards the student as a preceptor. Is the clinical rotation an observership, for instance, where the student simply follows and observes the preceptor? Or is it one where the preceptor delegates patient-care responsibilities to the student?

Action

Of the two issues described above, patient interaction is paramount. Student learning, while important in its own right, comes secondary to patient care. Consider if the patients are not bilingual and instead can only speak Mandarin. It makes no sense for the physician to speak in English if the patients cannot understand what is being said! The physician's primary role is to treat the patients and he or she cannot do so without being understood. If this is the scenario, then there are several options the student can take. Firstly, the student can request the physician to translate what is being said into English, thereby facilitating both patient care and student learning simultaneously. However, this may only be suitable if the number of Mandarin-speaking patients is limited. If the physician has to do this for every patient or if the break for translation interferes with patient-rapport and care, then it may not be a feasible process. In this case, the student may request to either be responsible only for English-speaking patients or request a transfer to another site where this communication problem is minimal.

Assuming that it is the physician who is not fluent in English and prefers to use Mandarin, the student may bring up this issue with the preceptor as well as with the Clerkship office at his university. Perhaps the preceptor should not have volunteered or been assigned to have a student if it was known there would be communication problems beforehand.

While physician-patient interaction is important, the student also needs to understand the preceptor and patients, especially if there is responsibility delegated for patient care. It is not unreasonable to expect the preceptor to facilitate the student's learning and to go out of his or her way to ensure that all rotation learning objectives are met, especially if the physician volunteered to have a student on-site.

Take Initiative

While this case describes a difficult situation where the student is isolated due to language barriers, it does provide a useful opportunity to learn from a new and difficult challenge. With the diverse multicultural patient population present in our hospitals today, situations such as these arise on a frequent basis. It is often that the patients do not understand English and/or the physicians do not understand the patient's mother-tongue. The student can take this opportunity to learn about possible solutions if such a case were to arise in the future.

One solution is the use of translator services. Non-English speaking patients are often accompanied with an official translator who is well-versed in medical terminology. These services are available at major health centers across Canada. If an official translator is not available, the physician may choose to have a patient's family member present to interpret. Although this is not always an ideal situation, it does help bridge the language gap.

Additionally, patients on the ward are often given picture cards to describe what they are experiencing. They may use pictures to describe their mood, whether they feel pain, if they are hungry, etc. While these may not be useful in a family-practitioner's office, it does serve to simplify basic patient management.

By taking the above steps, the student can not only facilitate his own learning, but also aid in providing a better experience for learners that follow.

Case 8. You are a third year medical student completing a clinical rotation in the diabetes clinic. One evening you receive a friend invitation on Facebook. Upon reviewing the friend request you realize that it's coming from a patient in the diabetes clinic. He is trying to connect with you on Facebook so he could ask you questions about applying to medical school. Would you accept him as a friend on Facebook?

Summary

_____

_____

Key issue(s)

_____

_____

Seek more information

_____

_____

_____

Action

_____

_____

_____

_____

Take initiative

_____

_____

_____

_____

Prompt questions

What do you think will happen if you reject this person on Facebook?

Is it possible to engage in a professional relationship with a patient on social networking sites?

Key issue(s)

- Doctor-patient relationship: crossing professional boundaries.
- Patient privacy and confidentiality issues.

Seek more information

- Is the patient aware of privacy issues related to social networking sites?

Action

- Have an offline discussion with patients who contact you via social networking regarding the confidentiality and privacy issues inherent in communicating in this manner.

- Discuss with patients the need to document doctor-patient communication in the medical record.

Take initiative

- Develop a personal social media policy to govern your interactions with patients via the internet and social networking sites.

Case 9. Fee splitting involves payment from one dentist to another for referring a patient. Do you think fee splitting should be forbidden in dentistry?

Summary

_____

_____

Pros

_____

_____

_____

Cons

_____

_____

_____

Your stance

_____

_____

_____

_____

_____

Take initiative

_____

_____

_____

_____

Case 10. You are a newly recruited camp counselor in charge of designing fitness programs for autistic children. On your way to work one morning, you witness your supervisor holding hands with a female who definitely looks to be a minor. What actions would you take in such sensitive situation?

Summary

Key issue(s)

Seek more information

Action

_____

_____

_____

_____

_____

Take initiative

_____

_____

_____

_____

Prompt questions

What do you think would happen if you report the supervisor?

Would you discuss this issue with your colleagues?

Key issue(s)

- Appropriateness of physical contact in a professional setting
- Stereotyping of non-verbal communication

Seek more information

- Who are the supervisor holding hands with? Is she actually a minor? Is she a camp member? Is she a family relative of the supervisor?
- Is the supervisor male or female?
- Does the supervisor mention anything about the incident, at work?
- What is the reason behind the physical contact? Determining the context here will define the rest of the scenario.
- The supervisor could simply be helping the 'minor' cross the street.

Action

- After seeking more information, take action if the interaction is inappropriate. This can be done by confronting the supervisor or bringing the issue to someone higher up.

- Furthermore, the minor's parents or guardians also need to be notified because this becomes a safety issue.

- Finally, if the issue is not resolved easily, the authorities need to be notified so they can take action.

**All these are only applicable if the physical interaction is inappropriate **

Take initiative

Establish clear guidelines to ensure that volunteers, staff and camp participants are familiar with appropriate personal-professional boundaries.

Case 11. You wrote a manuscript for publication, which you gave to your supervisor (principle investigator) for review. After a month, he gives it back to you with minor revisions and an additional name as an author: his wife's. Knowing that your supervisor's wife has had no involvement in preparation of your manuscript, what actions would you take?

Summary

_____

_____

Key issue(s)

_____

_____

Seek more information

_____

_____

_____

Action

_____

_____

_____

_____

_____

Take initiative

_____

_____

_____

_____

Summary

Here it seems that upon reviewing the manuscript, my supervisor has added his wife's name as an author. Furthermore, for some reason, he has not discussed his reason behind adding his wife's name, to the manuscript, with me.

Key issue(s)

Although this case contains several important issues such as professionalism, and conflict of interest, the central issue is integrity.

Seek more information

Prior to taking any actions it's essential that I seek more information and clear any misunderstandings that might have occurred. For example, one possibility is that my supervisor has added his wife's name by mistake. Given that most supervisors have several commitments, such as teaching, research, preparing grant applications and simultaneously reviewing several manuscripts, such possibility is highly probable. Thus, my supervisor might have simply mistaken my manuscript with another project in which his wife is involved. Another possibility is that, my supervisor's wife has actually had some involvement in the project and for some reason I have not been made aware of her contribution. Additionally, it's possible that my supervisor has newly been appointed and is not fully aware of guidelines in authorship.

Action

There are numerous plans of action I could utilize to resolve this issue: (1) I could escalate the situation and bring the issue to someone else's attention such as the faculty administrator, (2) turn a blind eye, and simply do nothing, or (3) I could contact the supervisor and work with him as team to resolve the issue.

All three plans of action have pros as well as cons which affect my decision. While the first two options might seem like an easy way out they have some major implications. Escalating the situation and reporting the supervisor to the faculty administrator could potentially damage my relationship with the supervisor (because the supervisor would not be happy if ever found out that I reported him without giving him a chance to explain), waste valuable resources (administrators effort to resolve the dilemma), especially if the issue ends up being due to a simple misunderstanding. Similarly, turning a blind eye would undermine my own integrity as well as the research group's. The third option, however, does not seem to have any major negative implications if it's executed appropriately.

Therefore, I would contact my supervisor, via email, telephone, or in person, and kindly make him aware of my concern. To do this, I would first thank him for his input and thoroughly reviewing the manuscript, and then I would simply ask him whether he has had an opportunity to review the list of authors for the project. In communicating with him it's imperative that I remain open-minded and maintain a professional style of communication (written or spoken). My next step would depend on my supervisor's response. For instance, if he responds by informing me that he has made an honest mistake or that his wife has actually contributed to the project, the matter is, more or less, resolved. In addition, if his wife has had minor involvement in the project, I can offer to write her name in the acknowledgment section of the manuscript. If, on the other hand, he unjustly insists that his wife's name remains as an author, I would conclude that he has a poor sense of integrity and will have to carefully take further actions.

The reason that I would be careful in my next step is that damaging my relationship with the supervisor is both unprofessional and undermines my goals as a student - because as you know, chances are that I would need him as a future reference or a mentor. Thus I would seek all my resources to resolve the issue in the most appropriate way. One option is to talk to my supervisor again and describe for him how I believe having an additional author who has had no contribution, undermines my efforts as it "dilutes" my involvement. Additionally, I would ask him what he would do, if he was in my situation. By asking him to consider my side of the issue, I can achieve several things: (1st) I would demonstrate that I respect him and value his advice, (2nd) I would demonstrate that I have a strong sense of integrity, and that I stand by my values.

However, if my supervisor still makes no effort to resolve this issue and provides no sensible explanation, it's plausible that he is using his position, as my superior, to intimidate or "bully" me and include his wife's name in the manuscript unjustly. In that case, I would utilize other resources including: asking advice from colleagues, or choosing option number one (discuss the issue with the director or someone else at a senior level).

Take initiative

I think, realistically, issues like this happen in many situations at work, school, or personal life. And in order to establish and maintain a positive relationship with colleagues and supervisors it's important to learn how to resolve them. Feeling pressured, some students might turn a blind eye and submit the manuscript without challenging their supervisors but by doing so they are actually dismissing their own values as well as damaging their own integrity. Additionally, such behavior could prove to have larger implications in circumstances which involve others such as patients.

Ultimately, as much as clear communication and trust are integral parts of one's relationship with his or her supervisor, I believe it's critical that students as well as supervisors are made aware of the underlying guidelines and regulations in their field from the very beginning. In this case, for example, if I the student, and the supervisor had discussed and both agreed to the guidelines of authorship prior to this dilemma, it would have been a lot easier to resolve the issue. Thus to ensure that such conflict does not arise again for myself or other students I would recommend my faculty to implement appropriate measures such as establishing an unbiased committee, consisting of faculty members and students, which reviews the authorship for all manuscripts prior to publication.

Case 12. You are an intern working in a busy hospital. A 29-year-old female patient, Natalie Iberian, is admitted to your unit after a car accident. Her chart indicates: concussion, fractured jaw, and severe blood loss. One of the interns points out to you that Natalie's 2-year-old son, Tommy, has been killed in the accident. As you begin your daily rounds, Natalie directly asks you about Tommy. Would you share the news with her?

Summary

_____

_____

Key issue(s)

_____

_____

Seek more information

_____

_____

_____

Action

_____

_____

_____

_____

_____

Take initiative

_____

_____

_____

_____

Prompt questions:

Is it ever reasonable to lie to a patient?

What do you think would happen if you disclose her son's death to her?

Case 13. During an early morning lecture one your professors, who is well-liked by most students, publicly makes fun of one your classmates who is taking a "power-nap" in class. Even though, you are not close friends with this particular classmate, you have heard that he is suffering from a severe sleeping disorder. What actions, if any, would you take in such situation?

Summary

_____

_____

Key issue(s)

_____

_____

Seek more information

_____

_____

_____

Action

_____

_____

_____

_____

_____

Take initiative

_____

_____

_____

_____

Prompt questions:

Does the fact that the professor is well-liked have an influence on your decision?

Is the student entitled to having naps in class when others are trying to learn?

Seek more information

- Is the student being disruptive to the class?
- Are there any set guidelines regarding class attendance?
- Is the student aware that he or she is falling asleep?
- Could the professor's remarks be interpreted as insults?
- Is the professor aware that the student is suffering from a severe sleeping disorder?

Action

-Help the student identify the cause of his sleeping problem. Help identify whether it is causing issues with others in the class.

- Problem solve with the student and possibly the professor if there is a tangible reason behind need for the power naps.

- Be careful in this case, however, as the classmate may take offense to someone prying about personal matters such as this. If there is resistance, be comfortable in backing off.

Take initiative

Establish clear guidelines regarding class attendance as well as students' behavior during lectures and ensure that students as well as teaching staff review such guidelines prior to the start of the course.

Case 14. In this station you will interact with another person to complete a task. Your role is to give verbal instructions to the person in the room so he or she can reproduce the knot as outlined below. The person in the room will rely only on your verbal instructions to reproduce the knot. Once you enter the room you will sit with your back against his or her back and will be provided a copy of the instructions below. You must take extra care that the other person does not see the diagrams and refrain from turning around during this exercise. Your performance will be evaluated by the evaluator who will be sitting to your left.

Step 1.

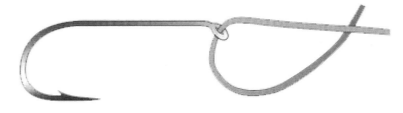

Step 2.

Step 3.

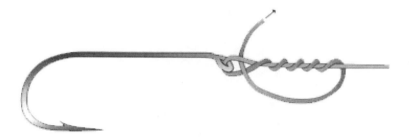

Step 4.

Step 5.

Step 6.

Step 1: Describe the task

_____

Step 2: Agree on a plan of Action

_____

_____

_____

Step 3: Anticipate difficulties

_____

Step 4: Give instructions

_____

_____

_____

_____

_____

_____

_____

_____

_____

_____

_____

_____

_____

Case 15. Many countries, including United States, Canada, and United Kingdom, have implemented a program termed travel nursing to alleviate nursing shortage in rural areas. Travel nursing enables nurses to travel to rural areas to temporarily work in various nursing positions. Discuss with the interviewer the advantages as well as the disadvantages of travel nursing in terms of health care quality and access.

Summary

_____

_____

_____

Advantages

_____

_____

_____

Disadvantages

_____

_____

_____

_____

Your stance

_____

_____

_____

_____

Take initiative

_____

_____

_____

_____

Advantages

- Alleviate some of the problems caused by the shortage of health care staff.
- Financially benefit nurses that work in rural areas.

Disadvantages

- Short term solution (not sustainable).
- Reduction in the number of nurses working in urban centers.
- The temporary nature of the nursing assignments might have a negative impact on the quality of care (as the nurses will not have enough time to complete training/orientation)

Take initiative

Utilize effective strategies that have been used by other countries to address health care quality and accessibility in remote areas. One example is health houses, which are informal sites set up in rural communities as the first stop for medical care, rather than an emergency room. They are staffed by community health workers (not doctors) who are responsible for vaccinations, administering medicine, etc.

Case 16. You are just finishing a 17-hour shift and are about to leave home. You feel extremely tired. The co-worker who is taking over from you is late and you are being called to review a patient's chart. You realize right away that the matter will take at least an hour to get resolved. What do you do?

Key issue(s)

_____

_____

Seek more information

_____

_____

_____

Action

_____

_____

_____

_____

_____

Take initiative

_____

_____

_____

_____

Prompt questions:

Is it ever acceptable for the co-worker to be late when he has such an important position in patient care?

Key issue(s)

- Physician fatigue.
- Problem solving.

Seek more information

- Whatever decision is taken has to be one that is best for patient outcome.
- One needs to know: the medical condition of the patient, if the condition is unstable and/or critical, the physician on-shift offers the best chance for a good outcome, so regardless of fatigue, the patient needs to be seen.
- Does the fatigued doctor feel comfort completing the task (reviewing the chart).
- Is there anyone else who is qualified to assist the fatigued doctor?
- Has the co-worker been late before? If so why?

Action

- Given an opportunity, identify why the co-worker was late. If it is a one-off issue, then it is of little concern. Small things happen all the time. If the issue is repeated over and over, then action has to be taken to identify and resolve the cause(s) for being late.

Take initiative

- Setup a 24 hour support line for physicians who are on call.
- Allow for overlapping of shifts to ensure that late physicians do not affect patient care. This is similar to the model employed

by physicians in some Emergency departments, where physicians coming off a shift have a 2 hr. overlap with physicians coming on shift.

Case 17. In most clinical settings LPNs (licensed practical nurses) often report to RNs (registered nurses). Robert, a patient, observes Natalie, an RN, speaking in an angry manner to Susan, an LPN. Natalie is criticizing Susan about her nursing care and how she takes too long to complete routine tasks. If you are the supervisor of the ward and such conflict is brought to your attention, how would you resolve it?

Summary

_____

_____

Key issue(s)

_____

_____

Seek more information

_____

_____

_____

Action

_____

_____

_____

_____

_____

Take initiative

_____

_____

_____

_____

Summary

A supervising nurse has an issue with a subordinate's working practices, particularly the time it takes for her to complete routine tasks.

Key issue(s)

I believe the main issue here is conflict resolution, a usual event in any workplace including the hospital environment. It is made difficult by the fact that the supervisor may not know the extent of the angry exchange - whether it is a one-time event or a continuation of past conflicts.

Seek more information

Before getting involved between the Natalie and Susan, it is important as a supervisor to glean the source of the conflict. This includes not only the information regarding the current argument, but also whether there have been past disagreements, with each other as well as other staff. This would provide some insight into the natures of both the RN and the LPN. Perhaps the conflict has less to do with medical tasks and more with personality differences. It is important to know this information beforehand prior to addressing the conflict.

If it is deemed that the issue has to do with medical and professional tasks, the next step would be to inquire about the details of the disagreement. What particular tasks does Susan have difficulty with? And why? Is it because of insufficient

95

training? Is it because of a flaw in methodology? Does Susan ask for help and support when she is unable to complete the tasks? Does Natalie do enough to instruct Susan? Are her expectations reasonable? Is her way of broaching the subject appropriate? How does she treat other LPNs?

Lastly, but perhaps most importantly, the supervisor has to inquire about how this affects patient management. For instance, time taken in an administrative task is not as critical as time wasted in patient care. The former may be an inconvenience whereas the latter is negligence.

Throughout this process, it is important to ensure privacy for those involved. Conflict resolution can quickly turn into a breach of professionalism, which in itself has the potential to affect entire careers. In other words, the supervisor, while being thorough in the information-gathering process, must also be sensitive to the needs of the employees working under his / her charge.

Action

After the information has been collected, it is time to make a choice on whether to get involved in the conflict or let Natalie and Susan sort it out themselves. This decision would be based not only on the RN's and LPN's wishes, but also how it affects other aspects of the professional team, particularly patient care.

Assuming that intervention is necessary, the first step is to establish a physical space where the supervisor can speak one-on-one with Natalie or Susan in privacy. It is important to speak with them individually, inviting their personal perspectives on the disagreement. Often, conflicts are a result of miscommunication and resolution requires only understanding of each other's views.

It is also the supervisor's role to establish boundaries, professional, personal as well as emotional. Conflict resolution in the workplace should focus on specific issues and behaviors and avoid generalized stereotyping of personalities. During the discussions, the supervisor should be fair and respectful of both the RN as well as the LPN, conveying full intention on conflict resolution, making sure to avoid taking sides and being biased. These things are best established through clear and coherent communication strategies. The supervisor should listen carefully to the details of the current and past disagreements, expect and accept their right to disagree with one another. The supervisor should invite Susan to describe why it takes long to do certain tasks and also ask Natalie on the timeframe she expects the tasks to be completed.

At this time, it would also help to ask whether there are any other factors, within the workplace or outside, that are interfering with the nurses' roles. Perhaps Natalie has a personal conflict that has made her easily irritable and quick to get upset. Perhaps Susan has external distractions that prevent her from working efficiently.

Once discussions have taken place with each nurse individually, the next step is to have a group discussion with both present at the same time. The conflict should be defined in specific terms to ensure that the discussion does not get side-tracked. A solution should be proposed that, again, involves specific steps to ensure clarity. For example, Susan's task might be to educate herself to improve on her particular deficiencies to increase efficiency in task completion, and Natalie's might be to control her angry outbursts and be forthcoming in offering help should she sense that Susan is having trouble. It is often best to offer alternative solutions as well. Perhaps the disagreement runs deeper than what was initially evident and Susan and Natalie may have to work different shifts to avoid future meetings. Whatever plan is eventually selected, a follow-up (possibly in the form of another individual or group meeting) should be in place to evaluate progress.

Take initiative

This scenario is interesting because of the broad scope of the topic of conflict resolution. There is no one right answer that is better than the rest. This provides an opportunity for the supervisor to improve his or her skills on conflict management and resolution. Dealing with disagreements is an integral part of daily life and a supervisor at a workplace has an essential role in acting as a third-person mediator. There are countless books, websites, informational videos, and presentations that are available that provide valuable strategies and useful tips when dealing with conflicts. Opportunities also exist for both Susan and Natalie. Emotional outbursts have no place in a professional environment such as a medical facility, and both Natalie and Susan may benefit from sharpening their conflict-resolution skills. Ultimately, patients are the ones who are most affected by the behaviors of the staff and nurses, the duty of patient care is paramount to any personal disagreements between individuals.

Case 18. You are a physiotherapist helping Mrs. Salderhoe, a 78-year-old patient, diagnosed with AIDS and end stage liver cancer. She is in severe pain and requests that you leave her alone and "let her have a peaceful death". You document her request and inform the supervisor. Several days later, one of your colleagues tells you that everyone in the unit believes that you have ceased treatment simply because you are afraid to contract HIV. Discuss with the interviewer how you would handle such difficult situation.

Summary

_____

_____

Key issue(s)

_____

_____

Seek more information

_____

_____

Action

_____

_____

_____

_____

_____

Take initiative

_____

_____

_____

_____

Prompt questions

Do you think it's necessary to discuss your reason for ceasing treatment with your colleagues?

Case 19. You are a well-established dentist working in an underserved area of town. A long term patient of yours asks you for advice about traveling to a third world country to save money on some costly cosmetic procedures. How would you discuss this issue with your patient?

Summary

_____

_____

Key issue(s)

_____

_____

Seek more information

_____

_____

_____

Action

_____

_____

_____

_____

_____

Take initiative

_____

_____

_____

_____

Prompt questions

Would your response change if the patient was seeking non-cosmetic procedures?

Key issue(s)

- Patient-directed care.
- Doctor-patient relationship.

Seek more information

- Where is the patient going for the procedures?
- How much information/experience does the dentist have regarding dental tourism? Has he had other patients who have gone that route?
- Has the patient explored all his options (less expensive clinics or financial support) in his own country?
- Are there others who have had success in similar situations?
- Are there any available data regarding treatment outcomes in third world countries?

Action

- Have an honest discussion with the patient regarding the benefits and risks of going to other countries for medical procedures.

- Find alternative sources of financial support such that the patient is able to have these procedures in his own country.

Take initiative

- Explore a variety of options so that people in the future with similar concerns have an adequate fund of knowledge to make an informed decision.

Case 20. A female patient comes to you complaining that one of your colleagues touched her inappropriately during a clinical visit. She is asking you whether or not she should press charges. What would you do in this situation?

Summary

_____

_____

Key issue(s)

_____

_____

Seek more information

_____

_____

_____

Action

_____

_____

_____

_____

_____

Take initiative

_____

_____

_____

_____

Prompt questions

Do you prefer to settle this case before a formal complaint is filed? Why?

Is your primary obligation to help the patient or your colleague?

How would your response change if the colleague in question was your supervisor?

Case 21. You are a physiotherapist who has been out of school for many years. Due to personal circumstances you move to a new city and look for a new job. The only available position is in a busy and well-established clinic, situated several blocks away from your residence. This privately owned clinic has goals set for each therapist to see at least fifteen patients a day. In spite of feeling very nervous about the workload, you begin to feel more comfortable as you gain more experience with your new position. One day you realize that you have made a mistake in managing a new patient. Upon assessing the situation, you feel certain that you will lose this much-needed job, which you financially rely on, if the clinic supervisor discovers your mistake. What would you do?

Summary

_____

_____

Key issue(s)

_____

_____

Seek more information

_____

_____

_____

Action

_____

_____

_____

_____

_____

Take initiative

_____

_____

_____

_____

Summary

A physiotherapist has made an error regarding a patient's care and feels that revealing the error will jeopardize his or her job. Further complicating the matter is the financial need of the therapist.

Key issue(s)

I believe the main issues here are those of integrity and patient care. Two competing goals are the therapist's own financial stability and the effect of error on patient treatment. The personality of the supervisor is also of concern as the scenario makes it appear that he or she is inflexible and intolerant of mistakes.

Seek more information

Before making a decision, it is necessary to find out the details of the error, particularly when it was actually made and what effect it had on patient management (is the patient still at risk?). A medical practice such as this one may witness errors of various kinds, some that are administrative in nature, others involving misdiagnoses, or even those that directly affect patient therapy. What specific type of error was made? In the event it was an administrative error such as a misspelled name, one can assume it would be easily correctable. If the error is one of the latter two types, then more steps need to be taken to correct it.

If the error was a diagnostic one such as a missed occult fracture on an X-ray, then it is the therapist's role to first explore why it was missed and how it will affect future management of the patient in question as well as other patients. Perhaps the error is such that it will have negligible change on current therapy. On the other hand, perhaps the error has a drastic impact on patient health and wellness. In either case, full disclosure is paramount.

Action

Once the details of the error have been understood and investigated, it is the therapist's duty to fully disclose the mistake to the patient. Discussing the error with the supervisor is a little bit more complicated and has more to do with the supervisor's role at the clinic. If the physiotherapist is solely responsible for his own patients or clients, then it may not be necessary to involve the supervisor (depending on the magnitude of the error, of course) and rather ensuring patient confidentiality. If the supervisor is responsible for those working under him or her, then disclosing the mistake is important for his or her job security as well.

Administrative errors are often of little consequence, other than the tedious task of correcting the information on file. This should be done promptly to ensure that no mistakes are made in treatment plan or in other aspects of patient management, for example: medical forms for insurance, etc.

Diagnostic errors are more complicated, as a treatment plan may already have been initiated. Again, disclosure to the patient is of utmost importance. Medical professionals, including therapists, are viewed as consultants. Their role is to advise patients, much as a consultant would advise a client. If an error is made, the patients have every right to know what happened, much as a client can demand the same from a consultant. The therapist should explain to the client why the old diagnosis was incorrect, whether it affects the client's health, how the new diagnosis was found, and how it all affects the management plan. Whether the supervisor finds out is secondary.

Treatment errors are perhaps the most important. A medical professional's role is first and foremost to do no harm. If a mistake has been made in treatment that has adversely affected a patient, then the error must be brought to light immediately. Again, the therapist must explain what the error was, how it was made, why it was made, and what is being done to correct it—in this case as well as in future cases.

With regards to the supervisor finding out, it would be much worse if he or she found out that an error was made and not disclosed or corrected. A therapist should not lose the job over it in a reasonable world, but things do not often work in that manner. Regardless, the therapist should inform the supervisor, making sure to explain things clearly and coherently. The explanation can take a similar form to that made to the patient, with emphasis on honesty and integrity. In this way, the therapist can cast himself in a favorable light as well as convey the full details of the error ensuring that steps are taken to prevent reoccurrence in the future. If, ultimately, the therapist loses the job, then it is an unfortunate event, but one that cannot supersede information disclosure on medical errors to patients.

Take Initiative

Any time an error takes place, there is an opportunity to learn something from it. Even something minor such as misspelling a name could have drastic implications on patient management. Using identification numbers or crosschecking spellings may help in preventing future mistakes. In medical practices, presentations could be given regarding errors to educate other staff and put together prevention policies and practices.

The error made by the therapist may have been made many times before, but it may have only been disclosed in this case. This is an opportunity to implement change and the therapist should not shy away from talking about the mistake because of fear of losing the job. In fact, this situation presents an opportunity to the supervisor as well, to learn from another's mistake rather than reprimanding him or her from the job.

A third facet is the legal side to this scenario. Patients often sue medical professionals when the feel that information has been hidden from them. Although this should not be the only motivation for full disclosure, it is still something that needs to be considered. Ultimately, integrity and honesty are two qualities that benefit and improve on patient care and full disclosure of errors is a necessary aspect of possessing both.

Case 22. You are an undergraduate student volunteering in a medical clinic situated in an underprivileged part of town. In your very first day you notice that the secretary often double books patients who are classified as "illicit drug-users". She explains to you that "these people rarely show up for their appointments". What would you do in such circumstance?

Summary

_____

_____

Key issue(s)

_____

_____

Seek more information

_____

_____

_____

Action

_____

_____

_____

_____

_____

Take initiative

_____

_____

_____

_____

Prompt questions

Should the clinic be held responsible for ensuring that patients attend their appointments?

How would this scenario change if the clinic was a non-for-profit organization?

In your opinion should patients be penalized for missing their appointments?

Key issue(s)

- Role of healthcare professionals.
- The ethics behind stereotyping and offering selective care.

Seek more information

- Why do the patients miss their appointments? Is it because they are illicit drug users or are they being segregated in the clinic (i.e. are they being treated appropriately by the staff)?
- What has been done so far to ensure they make it to their appointments?
- Are there any special incentives or punishments for people who don't make it to their appointments on time?
- Is the secretary aware that her comments regarding "illicit drug users" imply stereotype?

Action

- Determining the reason behind the missed appointments is an important step forward. Once that is known, several steps can be taken to try and improve patient compliance as well as how staff (including the secretary) interact with patients.

Possible plans of action include:

Turn a blind eye and finish your volunteer shift without taking any action. (Pros: definitely the easy way out, does not jeopardize your volunteer position. Cons: undermines your integrity, does not improve the situation)

Have a discussion with the secretary and let her know stereotyping is wrong. (Pros: makes the secretary realize her mistake, might slightly improve the situation. Cons: jeopardizes your volunteer position because the secretary will probably not be happy about being criticized by an undergraduate student)

Report the secretary to the clinic manager. (Pros: does not involve much effort on your part, might slightly improve the situation. Cons: jeopardizes your volunteer position)

Approach the scenario with an open-mind and avoid making snap judgments about the secretary. Ask her politely what her views are on patients missing their appointments and whether or not she is aware of the underlying issues. Let her know how important her role is and how she could be part of the solution as she is pretty much the first line of contact with the patients. (Cons: none, if done appropriately. Pros: enables you to evaluate the situation from the secretary's perspective and gauge whether or not she is willing to improve patient care and compliance.) If it turns out that she is uncooperative and does not seem to care about resolving the issue, the clinic manager could be involved.

Take initiative

- Incentives or fines can be put in place to ensure patients show up.
- The clinic may also need to become more inclusive for underprivileged populations, who often lack education and are uninformed about the benefits of medical care. Therefore, some form of program could be implemented to better educate the patients about their health and the importance of compliance.

Case 23. It's 3:00 am and you are coming back from a friend's birthday party. In spite of the heavy snow fall you decide to take the last bus home. You get on the bus using your student bus-pass and take a seat close to the driver. Three stops later you spot a 12-year-old girl waving at the bus. She appears to be extremely cold and tired. As she gets on the bus she checks all her pockets but can't find her bus-pass or money. She politely asks the driver to let her in without a bus-pass but the driver refuses and asks her to leave the bus. Given that you have no money on you, what would you do?

Summary

_____

_____

Key issue(s)

_____

_____

Seek more information

_____

_____

Action

Take initiative

Prompt questions

What would you do if you were the bus driver in this scenario?

What would you do if the 12-year-old passenger had gotten in the bus with a bus pass that you knew did not belong to her?

Case 24. You are volunteering in your local pharmacy when a 9-year-old boy asks you where he can find "some condoms". Would you tell him where they are?

Summary

_____

_____

Key issue(s)

_____

_____

Seek more information

_____

_____

_____

Action

_____

_____

_____

_____

_____

Take initiative

_____

_____

_____

_____

Prompt questions

What are some factors that one should consider when selling condoms to a 9-year-old?

What do you think would happen if you don't tell him where the condoms are?

Key issue(s)

Acting in client's best interest and utilizing effective communication skills to provide an adequate level of information to a child.

Seek more information

- Are there any regulations against selling condoms to children?
- Does the boy know what condoms are and how they are used? -
- Additionally, does he state why he wants to purchase them?
- He might want them for a school project or simply to use them as balloons!
- Is the boy purchasing the condoms for himself or someone else?
- Is the boy accompanied by an adult?
- Is there adequate proof that the boy is actually 9 years old?

Action

- Regardless of the underlying issues the 9 year old has every right to purchase condoms.
- The volunteer can offer him advice on: what condoms are, how they work, how they should be used, etc.

Take initiative

- Design relevant sexual education that caters to children. The reality is that in spite of not being sexually active, many children are curious about sex.

Case 25. You are volunteering in the medical unit at the local hospital. Your role as a volunteer is to talk to patients and keep them company. One evening a fellow volunteer asks you to cover her shift. She tells you that she is scared and feels uncomfortable to talk to one particular patient named Mr. Albert. Upon reading his chart, you realize that Mr. Albert is a newly admitted HIV positive patient. Furthermore, being an out-of-province patient he has no one to visit with him. What actions would you take?

Summary

_____

_____

Key issue(s)

_____

_____

Seek more information

_____

_____

_____

Action

_____

_____

_____

_____

Take initiative

_____

_____

_____

_____

Prompt questions:

How would the situation change if Mr. Albert was not HIV positive but suffered from alcoholic cirrhosis (liver disease caused by long-term alcohol abuse)?

Key issue(s)

- Social stigma regarding patients with communicable diseases, especially AIDS.
- Role of volunteers.

Seek more information

- Why is the fellow volunteer afraid to talk to Mr. Albert? Is she afraid to contract HIV?
- Is she afraid that other volunteers would judge her if she talks to someone with AIDS?
- Is she overwhelmed by the workload?
- Does she have an adequate understanding of communicable diseases, especially AIDS?
- Is she volunteering because she truly wants to or is it for school purposes only?

Action

Depending on the information gathered there are a few options in terms of how to proceed:

- Simply cover for her and don't discuss the matter with anyone. (Cons: the fellow volunteer will not learn anything and the situation is likely to happen again in the near future. Pros: the patient will benefit from the much needed companionship)

- Speak to the fellow volunteer and make an effort to help her understand the situation better. Educate her about AIDS and AIDS related stigma and discrimination. Highlight how valuable her role is in Mr. Albert's care. Offer to accompany her during the visit. (Cons: the fellow volunteer might get the impression that you do not want to help her, she might feel like she is being pressured. Pros: enable the fellow volunteer in stepping out of her comfort zone, permanent solution if successful, benefits the patient)

Take initiative

While advances in medicine and drug therapies have enabled us to treat and address many biological symptoms that are associated with AIDS, consequences of stigma and discrimination are wide-ranging: being shunned by family, peers and the wider community, poor treatment in healthcare and education settings, an erosion of rights, and irreversible psychological damage.

Thus, it's necessary that the general public as well as those involved in delivering care (including volunteers) are well educated about medical as well as the social implications of communicable diseases.

Case 26. Mrs. Boel is a 36-year-old psychiatrist who has been involved in a horrific motor vehicle accident and as a result is admitted to the emergency department. In addition to severe blood loss, she has lost major facial tissue and severely fractured both her legs in multiple places. Upon assessment, it's determined that due to the extent of damage both her legs must be amputated. The patient can barely speak but is able to communicate with the health care staff through writing. When asked to sign the consent forms for the amputation surgery, she writes on a piece of paper "I request not to be treated further". Should treatment be terminated?

Summary

_____

_____

Key issue(s)

_____

_____

Seek more information

_____

_____

_____

Action

_____

_____

_____

_____

Take initiative

_____

_____

_____

_____

Summary

A patient is making a request to terminate care by a physician, even though it is deemed to be detrimental to her overall recovery process. The case is further complicated by the fact that the patient is a health care professional herself.

Key Issues:

There are two major issues presented in this case. The first is the rights of patients in directing their care and the second is the concept of quality of life versus quantity.

Seek More Information

Before any treatment is provided to a patient, consent must be obtained. This may be implied, verbal, written, or through a proxy. In this case, the patient has refused to give consent. Informed consent has four major components. First, the patient in question must have the capacity to provide consent. In other words, they must be in sound mind and offer sound judgement. Whether a person has capacity is usually apparent from other symptoms they may present with at the time. Family members may provide collateral history noting odd behaviors that are present. Delirium is often an issue post-trauma and is often identified by bedside nursing care staff. A qualitative test is to assess a person's wishes based on what any reasonable person in their place would do.

The second component of informed consent is full disclosure by the medical practitioner regarding any tests, treatments, or procedures, including expected benefits and risks. In this event, it would be the physician's responsibility to divulge all information to the patient. In the event that a patient is unconscious or incapable of providing consent (i.e. first condition is not met), a substitute decision-maker may make the decision on the patient's behalf. In emergency settings such as the one described in this case, providing full detail on the procedures is often difficult due to the necessity of initiating life-saving procedures promptly; however, it is the physician's duty to provide this information to the best of his or her ability.

The third component of informed consent is that the patient must comprehend all information provided. Again, this issue of "competency" is tied to the first component, capacity. The patient must be competent enough to make these decisions. Consider an example if the above psychiatrist spoke in Mandarin only and could not understand the risks or benefits of the procedure as outlined by the physicians. Even though she has full mental capacity and is functioning at an appropriate level, she cannot make a decision because she has not comprehended the information.

The final component is that any decision made must be voluntary, without any coercion or duress. In my opinion, this is of the utmost importance, as the decision maker must choose on his or her own accord, and not because of external pressure from others. Examples of external pressure include friends, family, or cultural, religious obligations. Care must be taken in this case to ensure that Mrs. Boel is not under any coercion from any source including the healthcare team.

Another important segment of this case is the concept of quality of life. While Mrs. Boel's amputation may seem a reasonable course of treatment, it may impair her quality of life significantly. Leg amputations for a wheelchair-bound patient would have drastically different consequences than for an athlete or a physical laborer. We need to ask what matters in Mrs. Boel's life because a decision that may seem contradictory to her physical ailments may actually be supported when put in context with her overall condition.

Action

Once all the information is collected and divulged to Mrs. Boel, a decision can be made on the stated grounds for informed consent, which I mentioned earlier. If Mrs. Boel has been deemed to be of full capacity, has been told of the risks and benefits of the amputations, has understood the information provided to her, and is making the decision of her own free will, then it is the physician's and the health institution's responsibility to abide by her wishes.

If, however, Mrs. Boel does not fulfill any of the above criteria, then a substitute decision-maker must be selected to make a decision on her behalf. Consequently, it would be incumbent on the substitute decision-maker to meet the above criteria. If a substitute decision-maker cannot be found, then there are procedures whereby the hospital's ethics committee can make decisions for patients, as long as the decision is one that makes reasonable sense (i.e. what any reasonable person in that situation would do given the quality versus quantity trade-off).

Take Initiative

Decision making and informed consent are important yet, at times, difficult concepts to implement in a health care facility, especially in emergency situations. As a result, it would be prudent for physicians to utilize any resources that are available for perusal. For instance, administrative staff may work quickly to get a hold of patient families and contacts if a similar situation were to arise. This could be achieved by establishing a clear line of communication between physicians and administrative team. Furthermore, physicians should take greater effort in ensuring that patients understand all the information presented to them. Too often patients make decisions without understanding the full implications. Ultimately, it is patient care that is in question and it is the duty of everyone in the health care system to provide the best quality of care available.

Case 27. You are a cashier working in a newly established liquor store. One evening, while cleaning the shelves, a young lady asks you to help her carry four bottles of whiskey to her car. Once you arrive at her car she takes her coat off and places it in the trunk. She then asks you to place three of the bottles in the trunk and one in the passenger seat. As you place the last bottle in the car you notice that she appears to be pregnant. What would you do at this point?

Summary

_____

_____

Key issue(s)

_____

_____

Seek more information:

_____

_____

_____

Action

_____

_____

_____

_____

_____

Take initiative

_____

_____

_____

_____

Key issue(s)

- Advocating for someone's safety.
- Interpreting a situation from multiple perspectives.

Seek more information

- Is she really pregnant?
- Does she know she is pregnant?
- Is she purchasing the whiskeys for her own consumption or someone else?
- Is she under the legal age?
- Does she know drinking and driving is dangerous and illegal?
- Is there anything odd about her demeanor? Does she appear to be emotionally stable?

Take initiative

Have warning signs on liquor bottles or liquor stores which outline the dangers of drinking during pregnancy.

Case 28. James is a second-year Canadian medical student completing an anatomy elective in Saudi Arabia. On the first day of the elective he signs-up to observe an autopsy. Not being able to speak Arabic he asks his partner, Jamal, to translate for him. Once the procedure starts, Jamal makes several jokes about the cadaver which James finds very offending. In your opinion what should James do?

Summary

_____

_____

Key issue(s)

_____

_____

Seek more information

_____

_____

_____

Action

_____

_____

_____

_____

_____

Take initiative

_____

_____

_____

_____

Key issue(s)

- Treating patients with respect.
- Advocating for patients.
- Interpersonal relationship between medical students.
- The importance of cultural norms in ethical situations.

Seek more information

- Is James familiar with Jamal's culture? Perhaps it is more offensive in the western world.
- Is Jamal aware that he is offending James?
- Did other students hear Jamal's remarks? If so, were his remarks perceived as being offensive by them as well?
- How fluent is Jamal in English? It's possible that Jamal's remarks were not meant to be offensive (language barrier).
- Has the school hosted international students like James before?
- If so how did they describe their experience?

Take initiative

- Design follow-up surveys for students who participate in international rotations and relay the results to international partners.
- Bottom line is that cadavers have been donated for the good of medicine and medical students; therefore they are entitled to the same level of respect as patients.

Case 29. You are a senior manager in a busy primary clinic. A new trainee refuses to deal with a black client. How would you resolve such issue?

Summary

_____

_____

Key issue(s)

_____

_____

Seek more information:

_____

_____

_____

Action

_____

_____

_____

_____

_____

Take initiative

_____

_____

_____

Key issue(s)

- Stereotyping in medicine: does it have a role?
- Patient-doctor relationship.

Seek more information

- Is racism the sole reason for denial of care? The trainee might feel incompetent to treat this particular patient (i.e. racism might have nothing to do with her refusal).

- It is possible that the trainee has had some form of a traumatic experience involving someone of color, in the past (if this is the case the trainee might require support)
- Has the patient done anything inappropriate?
- Does the trainee have issues with other ethnicities?
- Can the new trainee justify his or her decision?
- Does the patient need immediate assistance?
- Is there anyone else that could attend to the patient?

Action

Before proceeding, ensure that the patient is stable and someone is attending to him or her.

Take initiative

- Ensure that trainees as well as staff discuss their personal issues regarding dealing with patients before they start working on the ward (include a section in the application form).
- Make the distinction between stereotyping to identify diseases and stereotyping to segregate patients.
- Raise awareness regarding racism in Medicine.
- Outline professional standards for new trainees and workers.
- Highlight that racism in itself will not be tolerated

Case 30. Your newly married best friend comes to your clinic complaining of male pattern baldness. Following some routine assessments you prescribe him an oral medication which has been shown to be safe for men but not for pregnant women. You explain to him that if his pregnant wife consumes or even comes in contact with the medication, their future child might have birth defects. He understands the warning but requests that you don't discuss his visit with his wife. Several months later his wife who has had an elective abortion and subsequently is experiencing chronic depression comes to your clinic and asks for help. What would you do?

Summary

Key issue(s)

Seek more information

Action

_____

_____

_____

_____

_____

Take initiative

_____

_____

_____

_____

Summary

A close friend has come to your clinic and was prescribed medication that could be teratogenic if it is handled by his pregnant wife.

Key issue(s)

The main issue here is that of patient confidentiality. What complicates the case further is that the patient in question is a close friend and him and his wife are well known to you.

Seek more information

There are some major complications in this case that should not have occurred had the situation been managed ethically from the start. In a medical practice, physicians are generally not suppose to treat family members or close friends, as it results in a conflict of interest. Often, incorrect diagnoses are made as personal emotions can cloud objective judgement.

The first step now is to determine what the details of the situation are. Why did his wife get the elective abortion? Had she handled the medication? What contributors were present that led to her depression? All these things can be discussed with husband and wife (separately) provided both are your patients. If the wife is not a patient, then the doctor may not inquire about personal information as it would be a breach of confidentiality.

Perhaps the abortion is completely unrelated to medication use. Perhaps the friend has already told his wife about the pills.

Maybe the wife's depression is due to an unrelated cause. These are important issues that need to be addressed prior to a decision being made.

Another issue that needs to be covered is whether the husband and/or wife are willing to share their personal medical issues with one another. Due to doctor-patient confidentiality, a physician may not disclose information to others unless given permission to do so.

Action

Once the details have been understood, the physician can make an educated decision. If the wife had the abortion due to a non-medical cause, then the problem with the hair-loss pills need not be addressed. This way, the physician can maintain confidentiality with the husband by not disclosing his medical conditions with his spouse.

If, however, the abortion was due to a defect, it would warrant further exploration. Details into the wife's and husband's family history would provide additional insight into genetic disorders that run in the family. These may explain the genetic defects in the child, perhaps more so than the teratogenic effects of the medication. If there are no other factors such as family history, smoking, alcohol history, or other maternal infections, the doctor is faced with a difficult conundrum.

One the one hand, a patient requests his medical conditions not be disclosed to his spouse. On the other, the patient's spouse is requesting help for something that could have been a direct result of her husband's medication. The physician has a responsibility to both, since both are his patients.

A relatively easy solution would be to call them together in the office and discuss the issues (provided they both agree to share personal information). Depression is a complex problem and it helps to talk about it with others in the room. Furthermore, the husband is an ideal person to help with her depression, as he will be around her most of all. Secondly, the husband's male-pattern baldness may not seem as pertinent an issue to him now, given the state of affairs that have taken place. He may, in fact, volunteer to disclose the information to his wife.

If, however, the husband refuses still to disclose information, the physician has no choice but to honour that request. He may advise the wife, though, to avoid touching any unknown substances including medications as a safety measure to avoid teratogenic effects. Such a request seems benign and still protects the husband's wishes.

Take initiative

This case is a good example of one of the most common problems faced by family practitioners, and physicians in general. Often, doctors treat multiple members of the same family, and it is difficult to maintain patient confidentiality. Most of the time, members may disclose information to one another, but there are times when this does not occur. For instance, teenage girls may not want to disclose that there are on the birth control pill. Boys may not want to disclose that they smoke. Members of a family may not want their chronic diseases disclosed. The physician, despite knowing all the details has to "forget" them at every patient encounter, ensuring that none of this information is given to those who are not privy to it.

Information disclosure and patient confidentiality are one of the major tenets of medicine and the physician can take this opportunity to learn more about this topic. While in today's health care many physicians are expected to keep up to date with the evolving scientific world, unfortunately the value of maintaining and/or improving ethical decision-making abilities is often overlooked. There is a variety of literature written on this topic and a number of presentations every year discussing this issue. It is important because it affects patient care, and patient care is paramount to anything else.

Case 31. It is final exam season and you are studying in the Quiet Study Room of your school's main library. An hour later another student joins your table and as soon as he unpacks his bag he reaches for his lunch box. Even though there are numerous NO-EATING-PERMITTED signs posted everywhere in the library, he starts eating his lunch right in front of you. What course of action would take?

Summary

_____

_____

Key issue(s)

_____

_____

Seek more information

_____

_____

_____

Action

_____

_____

_____

_____

_____

Take initiative

_____

_____

_____

Prompt questions

1) What would you do if the student is uncooperative and disregards your request regarding not eating in the library?

2) What would you do differently if one your professors was eating in the library?

Case 32. You are a first year nursing student shadowing a staff nurse in a tertiary clinic. During your first day you are asked to observe the nurse while she performs a routine venipuncture procedure (process of obtaining venous blood) on a twenty-five-year-old Chinese patient. While the nurse is preparing the equipments the patient loses consciousness and lays flat on the examining bed. She tells you "don't worry, everything is fine" and performs the procedure on the unconscious patient. What would you do in such circumstance?

Summary

_____

_____

Key issue(s)

_____

_____

Seek more information

_____

_____

_____

Action

_____

_____

_____

_____

_____

Take initiative

_____

_____

_____

Case 33 (Acting Station). Your best friend Allen has been preparing to compete in the National Triathlon Competition for the past 10 months. The competition starts in one hour. A mutual friend has called you asking for help. He states that in spite of sustaining a serious head injury, several hours ago, Allen is determined to take part in the competition. The mutual friend is worried about Allen's health and has asked you to talk to Allen. Please enter the room and greet Allen.

* **In this scenario Allen is instructed to not say much to the interviewee. Additionally, he insists that he wants to take part in the competition regardless of the consequences.**

Summary

_____

_____

Key issue(s)

_____

_____

Seek more information

_____

_____

_____

Action

_____

_____

_____

_____

_____

Take initiative

_____

_____

_____

Case 34. One evening you come home after an exhausting day at school. Upon entering your flat, which you share with two other flat mates, you smell a strong cigarette odour. The next day you ask one your flat mates if she knows who has been smoking in the apartment. She replies: "all I know is that it's not me". Additionally she tells you that being an ex-smoker she does not mind the smell. Not knowing your other flat mate very well how would you handle this situation?

Summary

_____

_____

Key issue(s)

_____

_____

Seek more information

_____

_____

_____

Action

_____

_____

_____

_____

_____

Take initiative

_____

_____

_____

Summary

In this hypothetical situation I have been asked to discuss how I would resolve a conflict between myself and my flat mate who is apparently smoking inside the apartment.

Key issue(s)

In my opinion, key issues in this case are conflict resolution and everyday problem solving.

Seek more information

Prior to taking any action, I think it's essential that I gather as much information as I can about the scenario. For example, it's possible that none of my roommates are at fault and that the odour is coming from our next door neighbour. Alternatively, given that many odours resemble second-hand smoke it's possible that what I think is cigarette odour might be the smell of burnt toast or something.

Additionally, there might be no regulations against smoking in the apartment, in which case it's totally justifiable if one of my flat mates is actually smoking inside the apartment.

Given all of the possible scenarios it's essential that I remain open minded and do not blame anyone, including my flat mates, and avoid making snap judgments before I establish the facts.

Action

Depending on the context and the information I mange to gather, there would be several different ways I could resolve this case. For argument's sake let's imagine that my flat mate was actually smoking in my 'non-smoking' flat. That leaves me with two options: report him to the landlord or somehow approach him myself to resolve the issue. Reporting him to landlord is definitely the most trouble-free option but it does have some drawbacks such as: potentially damaging my relationship with the flat mate (because if he ever finds out that I reported him without giving him a chance to explain he would most likely be offended). While approaching him myself is undeniably the more difficult option, it's advantageous in several ways: enables me to improve my people's skill as well as problem solving skills and most importantly gives me an opportunity to get to know my flat mate better and potentially establish a long-lasting friendship.

Consequently, I would approach my flat mate and tell him that I would like to talk to him about 'something'. Before delving into the issue I will get to know him a little bit by talking about school and what he is studying.

I will then explore whether or not he is aware that the apartment is a non-smoking apartment. If he it turns out that he is in fact unaware of the apartment's policy, the problem is more or less resolved. If on the other hand, he admits that he is smoking in spite of being aware of the non-smoking policy, the situation becomes more difficult. What I would do then is describe for him why I want him to stop smoking inside the apartment. For example, it's possible that I am allergic to second-hand smoke, or that I simply do not want to be exposed to it. At the same time it's important that I don't alienate him and respect his choice to be a smoker.

Additionally, one aspect which is fairly easy to overlook is the underlying reason why he is smoking inside the apartment. Is it because he simply does not care and is not courteous or is it because he is going through a rough time. Even though it's fairly difficult to probe the underlying reason without knowing the flat mate very well and being close to him, it certainly would help in arriving at an appropriate solution.

In summary I would try to reason with him and approach the situation as a friend rather than an angry flat mate. However, if he continues to smoke and makes no effort to compromise I would have no option but to ask him to move out at his earliest convenience or discuss the issue with the landlord.

Take initiative

I think this case highlights the importance of conflict resolution skills in life. The conflict in this case could have been avoided if the landlord or the building manager had thoroughly gone over the regulations with the tenants. Additionally, it would have been advantageous if the flat mates had gotten together in the beginning of the term and made sure that they all came to a mutual understanding regarding what's acceptable and what's not.

Case 35. You visit your general practitioner for a routine physical examination. Before beginning the examination he politely asks: "would it be alright if some of our medical students observe today's session?" You approve and he invites three students in the room. Half way through the session you realize that the doctor keeps asking the students if the "video quality is clear". Being curious you ask "what video are you talking about doc?" The doctor responds "oh we are broadcasting this session live on the big screen for the rest of the class". How would you handle such a situation?

Summary

_____

_____

Key issue(s)

_____

_____

Seek more information

_____

_____

Action

_____

_____

_____

_____

_____

Take initiative

_____

_____

_____

Prompt questions:

- What should the doctor have done differently in this case?
- What should the patient have done differently in this case?
- What is the best way to ensure that patients are giving informed consent?

Case 36. You are applying for acceptance into professional school and ask your long time graduate supervisor to write you a reference letter and mail it directly to the school. Several days later, you receive a letter in your mail box and realize that he has mailed you an extra copy of the letter by mistake. Shortly after, you receive an email from him directing you to discard the letter without reading it. Being curious you open the letter and realize that your supervisor has written a very negative reference letter which includes false information about your time in his laboratory. What would you do?

Summary

_____

_____

Key issue(s)

_____

_____

Seek more information

_____

_____

Action

_____

_____

_____

_____

Take initiative

_____

_____

_____

Summary

A confidential document is opened against strict instructions to disregard and discard. The document has serious implications about the future of the student in question.

Key issue(s)

The main issues here are breach of confidentiality and conflict resolution.

Seek more information

There are some major complications in this case that should not have occurred had the situation been managed ethically from the start. The letter received from the supervisor should never have been opened, as it violates the confidentiality afforded to a referee when writing a reference letter. The situation is made worse especially since there were strict instructions from the supervisor to discard the letter. While opening and reading the letter resulted in important information being found, the student in the scenario was never meant to find that information in the first place.

Now that the deed is done, there are two possible outcomes. First, the student may choose to do nothing and the supervisor need never know. Second, the student can confess that the letter was opened and read. Both scenarios may have negative outcomes with respect to the professional school application.

Given that the first choice is unethical (the student is essentially lying to the supervisor), the second option needs to be pursued. The student needs to contact the supervisor, inform him or her that the letter has been read, and probe about the reasons behind the negative content. This information gathering is very important because it will help define whether the reference letter contains facts or false information. What may initially seem incorrect to the student may be valid from the supervisor's perspective, and vice versa.

Action

Given the initial breach of confidentiality, the supervisor certainly has the right to ignore the student's request of an explanation for the negative content. However, this would be morally incorrect on the supervisor's part. He or she has an important role to play in the student's career and it would be irresponsible to write a negative review without providing a basis and an explanation for those comments.

If the supervisor's explanation does provide validity to the comments in the letter, then the student has no choice but to allow the letter to be incorporated as part of his application. If the comments are not valid, the student may attempt to reason and explain himself to the supervisor in an effort to change the contents of the letter.

If the information is in fact false, then either the supervisor or student may call the application office and request removal of the letter from the application file. If the student continues to use the letter as part of the application, the office has to be notified that the letter is no longer confidential and that the student has read it already.

Take Initiative

This case is a good example of one of the critical components of an admission application to a professional school: reference letters. Every year, a certain percentage of applications are rejected on the basis of poor reference letters. The student can learn from this and take steps to avoid a similar situation in the future. These steps may include: gathering of more information from the referee prior to asking for a reference letter, and providing adequate information to the referee regarding the student's academic as well as extracurricular activities.

The student may simply state that he is hoping for a 'positive' letter—most referees will inform the student whether they are comfortable writing such a letter. Another strategy is to provide a summary of one's time and interaction with the supervisor. This often helps them formulate a more personal letter and avoids false information.

In the case described above, it is likely that there is no good outcome and that the student learns a valuable lesson from this experience.

Case 37. Many would agree that a health care professional should be a model of health, but a significant percentage of healthcare professionals propagate a message that says, "Do as I say, not as I do". In your opinion, should health care professionals be held to a higher standard of health than the rest of us?

Summary

_____

_____

Key issue(s)

_____

_____

Seek more information

_____

_____

_____

Action

_____

_____

_____

_____

_____

Take initiative

_____

_____

_____

_____

THE END

MSC MEDICAL